PARENTAL SUBSTANCE MISUSE

Donald Forrester

with Sally Baker and Jane Hartley

Published by
CoramBAAF Adoption and Fostering Academy
41 Brunswick Square
London WC1N 1AZ
www.corambaaf.org.uk

Coram Academy Limited, registered as a company limited by guarantee in England
and Wales number 9697712, part of the Coram group, charity number 312278

Originally published by BAAF in 2012
Reprinted by CoramBAAF in 2017

British Library Cataloguing in Publication Data
A catalogue record for this book is available from the British Library

ISBN 978 1 907585 47 0

Project management by Miranda Davies, Publications Department, CoramBAAF
Designed and typeset by Fravashi Aga
Printed in Great Britain by the Lavenham Press

Contents

Acknowledgements

The production of this guide was greatly assisted by the hard work of Emma Atkins and Jayne Giaramita, who carried out extremely helpful reviews of the research evidence. Many thanks also to Florence Merredew, Health Group Development Officer at BAAF, for her input and helpful suggestions.

Note about the authors

Donald Forrester worked as a child and family social worker in inner London from 1991 to 1999. During this time he worked with many families in which there was parental substance misuse. Donald has published widely in this area, including key studies identifying the extent of the problem, outcomes for children and a body of work exploring effective practice with parents who have drug or alcohol problems. He is currently Director of the Tilda Goldberg Centre at the University of Bedfordshire. Donald is the father of three children, including one who is adopted.

Sally Baker has a publishing background. When she found that she spent most of her time fighting her adopted children's corners after they had come to live with her and her husband, she started getting involved with Adoption UK as a Buddy and Parent Consultant. She is an Associate at Family Futures and currently trains as a co-counsellor.

When **Jane Hartley** and her husband, Neal, met, adoption was a subject that came up really early. Jane had travelled and been exposed to a lot of poverty, which made her want to 'do her bit'. Neil felt that there were too many children around needing families: they didn't have to go off to make their own. They consider themselves very lucky because they have done both.

The series editor

The editor of this series, **Hedi Argent**, is an established author/editor for BAAF. Her books cover a wide range of family placement topics; she has written several guides and a story book for young children.

Looking behind the label...

Jack has mild learning difficulties and displays some characteristics of ADHD and it is uncertain whether this will increase...

Beth and Mary both have a diagnosis of global developmental delay...

Abigail's birth mother has a history of substance misuse. There is no clear evidence that Abigail was prenatally exposed to drugs but her new family will have to accept some kind of developmental uncertainty...

Jade has some literacy and numeracy difficulties, but has made some improvement with the support of a learning mentor...

Prospective adopters and carers are often faced with the prospect of having to decide whether they can care for a child with a health need or condition they know little about and have no direct experience of. No easy task...

Will Jack's learning difficulties become more severe?
Will Beth and Mary be able to catch up?
When will it be clear whether or not Abigail has been affected by parental substance misuse?
And will Jade need a learning mentor throughout her school life?

It can be difficult to know where to turn for reliable information. What lies behind the diagnoses and "labels" that many looked after children bring with them? And what will it be like to live with them? How will they benefit from family life?

Parenting Matters is a unique series, "inspired" by the terms used – and the need to "decode them" – in profiles of children needing new permanent families. Each title provides expert knowledge about a particular condition, coupled with facts, figures and guidance presented in a straightforward and accessible style. Each book also describes what it is like to parent an affected child, with adopters and foster carers "telling it like it is", sharing their parenting experiences, and offering useful advice. This combination of expert information and first-hand experiences will help readers to gain understanding, and to make informed decisions.

Titles in the series will deal with a wide range of health conditions and steer readers to where they can get more information. They will offer a sound introduction to the topic under consideration and offer a glimpse of what it would be like to live with a "labelled" child. Most importantly, this series will look behind the label and give families the confidence to look more closely at a child whom they otherwise might have passed by.

Keep up with new titles as they are published by signing up to our newsletter on www.corambaaf.org.uk/bookshop.

Shaila Shah

Introduction

This book is intended to help those who are caring for or plan to
care for a child affected by parental alcohol or drug problems, as
well as professionals who support them. While it is based on the
latest research evidence, the intention is to make the findings as
clear and accessible as possible. Key points and the implications of
findings are highlighted in a series of boxes illustrating the practical
issues arising from the research evidence.

It is important to be clear about the risks for children associated
with parental drug or alcohol misuse. Much of this guide is
concerned with helping you to decide whether you should care
for a child whose parents misused, and provides information on
the sort of issues you might encounter and how you should or
could deal with them. All too often, publications dwell on the
risks associated with such children and the reality of the children
involved becomes lost; they become like a bundle of actual or
potential problems. Above all else, children whose parents have

misused drugs or alcohol are children. Like all children, they need love and boundaries, not to mention patience, attention, care and the myriad other things that parents and carers need to provide for children to thrive. Sometimes they will need not only excellent care, but also possibly specialist input to address specific problems. Yet this does not detract from the fact that, like any child, they will bring laughter and love and their own unique characters into the families they join. This guide has much to say about problems and challenges, but it also seeks to hold on to the positives.

As far as we are aware, adopted children whose parents misused drugs or alcohol do not have any more problems than any other adopted children. All adopted children are at risk of higher levels of various difficulties when compared to the general child population. For some, these can be very serious but for many – probably the majority – the outlook is relatively positive. The pattern of "risks" varies according to the child's specific circumstances and there are particular risks relating to alcohol- and drug-using parents. One clear piece of research evidence is that a caring family that loves and nurtures a child is the single factor most likely to help them achieve their full potential. Recognising this does not mean one should be naïve about the prognosis for any particular child. But it does help us to recognise the extraordinary contribution that so many adoptive and foster families make to helping so many children overcome their tough start in life – as illustrated by the adoptive parents' stories that make up the second half of this book.

The first section has three chapters: the first covers general issues around substance misuse and children entering care; the second looks at the impact on children of exposure to substances during pregnancy, including both specific effects (such as Foetal Alcohol Syndrome) and more general issues (such as genetic susceptibilities); the third makes recommendations for carers and professionals following from a review of the evidence.

The second section comprises two first-hand accounts from adoptive parents of children whose mothers misused drugs or alcohol. Their stories are not "typical" of adoptions – indeed there is no "typical" adoption – but they describe some of the most challenging situations that carers may have to deal with. As such, they are particularly illuminating. They also show what a difference a loving family can make for children, and demonstrate the character and strengths that children themselves bring to the families they join.

UNDERSTANDING DRUG AND ALCOHOL MISUSE AND ITS EFFECTS ON CHILDREN

DONALD FORRESTER

CHAPTER 1

Use, misuse, addiction and recovery

The parents of almost all children needing adoption or long-term foster care have problems that have led to their children requiring a home elsewhere. Parental misuse of drugs or alcohol is one of the most common of these problems. Research suggests that between 40 and 60 per cent of children requiring permanent alternative care are affected by parental substance misuse (PSM). This chapter provides background information and examples of the types of issues that arise in connection with PSM. It is intended to help people understand the complex nature of substance misuse, the ways in which it interacts with other difficulties, and the reasons why this results in parents being unable to care for children. It is hoped that it will support readers in understanding:

- the reasons for children entering care;

- the broader context within which substance misuse takes place;

- the inter-relationship between substance misuse and other problems

- the difficulties that these relationships create for producing clear research findings on its impact on children.

What is substance use and misuse?

This guide refers to "alcohol and drugs" as if they were different. In fact, alcohol is a drug. However, its history, patterns of use and legal status mean that in practice people often talk about alcohol differently. This book therefore refers to alcohol separately from other drugs. Where reference is made to alcohol and/or other drugs together, the term "substance" is used. Some information on cigarettes (which combine a variety of drugs and poisons) is also included. This is rarely a focus for concern – and it is unusual for it to be identified when information is provided about children – but in fact it is one of the more dangerous drugs for unborn children to be exposed to. More basic information on different common drugs is provided in Box 1, Chapter 2.

It is worth defining some of the terms used in relation to drug and alcohol. These include:

- **"Use"** of a substance carries no judgement: it is simply a factual description. The vast majority of adults use alcohol and many use illegal drugs, but few of these people cause themselves or others significant problems.

- **"Misuse"** or **"abuse"** or **"problem"** drinking/drug-
   taking refer to use of a substance that is causing the user or others a problem. The nature of this problem can vary, including for instance, health and relationship

8

difficulties or getting into trouble with the police. Given that the children we are looking at have come into care, it seems reasonable to assume that many of their birth parents "misused substances" and this tends to be the term used in this book. Misuse is different from "addiction" or "dependence".

- The term **"addict"** or **"alcoholic"** is used where people have a strong subjective feeling that they cannot control their drinking or drug-taking. These terms are controversial because they tend to be associated with disease models for understanding "addiction". In the academic community debate has raged about what addiction is, the extent to which it can be considered to be an illness, different types of "addiction" and the best ways of helping those with an addiction. Most of the parents of children who enter care where drugs or alcohol were an issue will be addicts, but this is not true for all. For some, use may constitute binges that are linked to other problems in the family.

- Physical and/or psychological **"dependence"** is produced when sustained and usually heavy use of a substance over a period of time results in withdrawal effects when the substance stops being used. There are often physical symptoms associated with such withdrawal (for instance, shakes, sweats, etc.). However, at least as important are the psychological elements (such as intense craving). Dependence is an important element of "addiction" but is a narrower term.

Patterns of use vary between individuals and tend to vary across substances. Some substances are characterised by steady use, which can be low or heavy (for example, cigarettes, heroin and, for some people, alcohol). Others tend to be used in relatively heavy "binges" followed by recovery periods (for instance, cocaine, crystal meths and, for some people, alcohol).

One key factor to consider is that substance use and misuse are so widespread that it is likely that most children adopted or fostered for "other" reasons will have had parents who used various substances. This is particularly true for alcohol and tobacco. Information about substance use during pregnancy should therefore be collected for all children in care, not just those whose parents are identified as misusing.

The extent and nature of parental substance misuse in the UK

The UK has one of the highest levels of problem drug and alcohol use in the world. It is difficult to know exactly how many children are affected; after all, researchers are unlikely to get honest answers if they knock on people's doors and ask about substance use and children's welfare. Research tends to be based on estimates drawn either from more general surveys of the population or specific studies of adults known to services. In general, it appears clear that very substantial numbers of children have one or more parents with a serious drug or alcohol problem. The figure seems likely to be in the region of one million children living with a parent with an alcohol problem and around 250,000 having a parent with a drug problem. Looked at another way, eight to 15 per cent of children are affected, so in an average classroom of 30 children, two to four will be going home to a parent with a serious drug or alcohol issue. The vast majority of these children remain with their families – less than five per cent of children whose parents misuse substances come into care. These tend to be the children of parents with the most severe drug or alcohol problems.

Heavy or problem drinking or drug-taking by parents affects parenting in two ways. Firstly, there is the direct impact of the substance use on the parent's ability to care for the child, either when they are intoxicated or through the after effects of intoxication (such as hangovers, withdrawal or come-downs). There are variations in the ways in which different substances may influence parenting, depending on how they tend to influence behaviour. The three most common substances that lead to children being removed are alcohol, heroin and "crack" cocaine. The impact of alcohol varies enormously between individuals and even for one person on different occasions. It sometimes causes drowsiness and loss of consciousness; it can lead to people becoming emotional and affectionate, or violent or disinhibited. Heroin is a depressant. Although intoxication with heroin is generally associated with individuals becoming drowsy and often losing consciousness, heavy users can behave relatively normally when using. Crack cocaine is a stimulant and is linked to disinhibited behaviour. Violence is not uncommon in crack users and heavy use can be linked to feelings of paranoia (see Box 1 in Chapter 2 for further information).

The second way in which substance misuse impacts on parenting is that the prioritisation of the substance can lead to the child's needs being neglected and can lead to chaotic family life. One way of conceptualising this is to understand that for the parent with an addiction, their main relationship is with their substance of choice; their concern for their child comes second. Children may experience not only neglect of their physical and emotional needs, but also the unavailability or unpredictability that can go with a parent who puts drink or drugs before their child. It can also be an issue during pregnancy. Most women who use alcohol or illegal drugs stop or significantly reduce use at this time. A minority find this impossible, putting their children at increased risk of numerous problems.

Parental substance misuse (PSM) and children entering care

There is still relatively little research on the extent and nature of

PSM in the families known to children's services. However, a few factors are worth noting:

- Children whose parents misuse substances are particularly likely to be young; most babies subject to care proceedings have been affected by parental drug issues, while parental alcohol issues are very common for toddlers (2–5), although found at all ages.

- Substance misuse is rarely the only issue in the families. Rather it tends to interact with a range of other problems, such as domestic violence or mental health issues.

- Assessing substance misuse issues is particularly difficult for social workers and other professionals. Parents will often make attempts to overcome substance problems and look after their children, and it is not easy to assess whether they will succeed or sustain changes.

Challenges for research and practice

This section outlines the difficulties in exploring the impact of parental substance misuse on children. These are not simply academic issues; they underline the clearest single finding in this area, namely that we know that use of substances during pregnancy is associated with a large number of problems for children later in life, but it is impossible to predict what the impact will be on any specific child. Indeed, our knowledge tends to be remarkably limited. The implications of this are discussed in depth below, but the lack of definite facts is probably the single biggest challenge facing carers and professionals in this area.

The problem for research is that substance use is not an isolated issue; it is strongly linked to a whole host of other problems. For instance, misuse often involves a variety of drugs and alcohol in different quantities. Most drug users also smoke, which is known to be independently harmful to babies. In addition, women in these situations are often living in considerable poverty. It is common for them not to take good enough care of themselves, so they often don't attend for prenatal care, miss out on taking vitamin supplements and they may not be eating adequately. They are especially likely to be involved in activities such as sex work, with related health problems. Many are experiencing violence, the level of which usually increases during pregnancy (exposing the unborn child to further risks).

When children are born, the parents are often living in extremely poor accommodation and circumstances. Their substance misuse may contribute to their inability to parent their child adequately; there is a strong body of evidence that suggests that the abuse and neglect suffered by the children of substance-misusing parents is more harmful to them than exposure to drugs and alcohol in utero.

Finally, these children are likely to be at increased genetic risk of certain problems. The most obvious is a greater risk of alcohol addiction, but there also appears to be a genetic element to the development of various types of antisocial or challenging behaviour (including attention and hyperactivity issues).

As if all of these disadvantages were not enough, services to help families change will have been offered, often over some time. This may mean that children have experienced several changes of carer with the ensuing disruption and uncertainty this can entail. With the benefit of hindsight, it might be tempting to see such attempts at supporting families to stay together as putting the child at risk of harm. However, this ignores the significant number of families kept together by effective services and the impossibility of accurately predicting which families will be able to achieve positive changes.

SECTION 1

13

The complexity of these issues underscores the fact that we cannot predict the impact that specific substances taken during pregnancy may have on unborn children. Even in animal experiments, when mice are given the same exposure to alcohol, the outcomes vary enormously between different mothers and their offspring: some seem very resilient while others appear vulnerable. Add in the huge diversity of real people in complex and difficult social situations, and it becomes impossible to know what the impact on specific children will be.

It is important to note that a statistically significant increase in the likelihood of a specific outcome does not mean that it is *probable*. For instance, Attention Deficit Hyperactivity Disorder (ADHD) is the most common behavioural disorder in the UK, affecting from three to nine per cent of children. Evidence suggests that maternal drug misuse may increase the likelihood of the disorder by between 50 and 100 per cent. This means it is likely to be present in from five to 18 per cent of children whose mothers misused drugs in pregnancy; it is therefore probably absent in about 90 per cent. At the same time, for many of the problems most clearly identified as substance related, there is strong evidence that good parenting and the passage of time reduce the likelihood of a problem developing.

It is a tribute to the tenacity and spirit of children that despite these many disadvantages so many of them turn out so well in new families. Children have reserves of resilience and a capacity to form relationships and heal wounds that allow most of them to bounce back from even multiple disadvantages if their foster or adoptive carers provide the love and discipline that encourage them to thrive.

CHAPTER 2

The impact of maternal substance misuse in pregnancy

This chapter provides a summary of research evidence on the impact of parental substance misuse on children. The primary focus is on use during pregnancy, though environmental and genetic issues are also touched on. Rather than supplying detailed information on every condition that might be linked to PSM, this chapter provides:

- an introduction to the key issues for children who have been linked to substance use;

- an appreciation of the similarities and differences between various substances;

- an indication of the most important factors that may increase or reduce risks for children.

The substances reviewed are those most commonly found in adopted children. These are:

1   Depressants
   ● alcohol
   ● tranquilisers and sedatives
   ● opiates – heroin, methadone, morphine

2   Stimulants
   ● Cocaine/crack cocaine
   ● Amphetamines

3   Hallucinogenic/psychedelic drugs
   ● cannabis

4   Tobacco/cigarettes

Box 1 provides some basic descriptive information about different substances that are commonly identified as problems in care proceedings.

It is important to remember that women rarely use only one substance. Smoking is common among people who misuse substances, cocaine and alcohol are often used together and it is usual for those using heroin or crack cocaine to also use other legal and illegal drugs. Despite high levels of use, some substances such as ecstasy and LSD do not seem common among the families of children entering care. Others, such as "crystal meth" and khat are comparatively rarely used in the UK at present. In general, very little is known about the implications of parental use for most of these substances.

BOX 1

Types of drug and common effects
(adapted from Forrester and Harwin, 2011)

A wide range of drugs is used. These include cannabis (in

a variety of forms), LSD, ecstasy (also known as MDMA), hallucinogenic mushrooms, and a range of prescribed medications that can be misused. Even common household substances like glue and nutmeg are misused. However, the most common concerns during pregnancy relate to tobacco, alcohol, heroin and crack cocaine.

Combinations of drugs can produce complex and unpredictable effects. Illegal drugs often vary in their strength and can be mixed with other substances. Effects vary by individual and the situation they are in. The following categorisation, based on information from the Drugscope website, www.drugscope.org.uk (2009), describes broad types of effect.

1. Depressants

Depressants are drugs which slow down the central nervous system to suppress neural activity in the brain. In large quantities depressants make people feel sleepy. They are dangerous because very large doses can lead to a fatal overdose as the vital systems of the body like breathing are slowed to the point where they stop.

The three main types in this category are:

- alcohol
- tranquilisers and sedatives
- opiates

Alcohol

Although alcohol depresses the central nervous system, light use can appear to have the opposite effect (for instance, light drinking may reduce anxiety and inhibitions). Heavier drinking negatively affects physical and mental functioning, and can produce vomiting, unconsciousness and even sometimes death. It is also linked to erratic and disinhibited behaviour (including, in some individuals, violence). Long-term heavy use causes a variety of health-related problems, particularly liver damage. Alcohol can cross the placenta and produce serious damage to babies in the womb.

Tranquilisers and sedatives

Tranquilisers and sedatives are medications that are legally prescribed by doctors. Tranquilisers produce feelings of calm and reduce or remove negative feelings and anxiety. Examples are the diazepam family such as valium and lorazepam. Barbiturates are sedatives prescribed to help people sleep. They are both highly addictive and when combined with alcohol can be particularly dangerous.

Opiates

These include heroin, methadone and morphine.

Heroin can be smoked or injected. Methadone is generally prescribed as a heroin replacement in liquid or pill form. Morphine is used medically as a painkiller.

Heroin initially produces feelings of pleasure and well-being and detachment from pain, anxiety or difficult emotions. Frequent users tend to report fewer of the positive effects from use. It can lead to individuals being unaware of their surroundings or becoming unconscious. Used regularly, all the opiates can be psychologically and physically addictive, though some people may use them without becoming dependent. Methadone prevents the feelings and physical effects associated with withdrawal but used as prescribed does not produce the positive feelings associated with heroin.

Withdrawal from opiates can include physical symptoms such as vomiting, sleeplessness, cramps and acute flu-like symptoms. Intense cravings for the drug may be as, or more, difficult to cope with. Physical symptoms usually peak within three days but can persist longer, with anxiety and insomnia particularly likely. Cravings can persist for far longer, and can appear acutely months or years after the individual has stopped using.

2. Stimulants

A stimulant is a drug which speeds up the central nervous system to increase neural activity in the brain. They tend to make people feel more alert and awake and are sometimes called "uppers". Examples are amphetamines, cocaine and crack, caffeine and ecstasy.

Amphetamines, cocaine and crack (a derivative of cocaine) produce feelings of euphoria, confidence, sociability, extreme happiness and energy. They can reduce inhibitions, leading individuals to become very talkative and feel confident, though their behaviour can also be unpredictable and their mood volatile. For some users this can be linked to an increased likelihood of violence. Stimulants tend to be taken for one or more days (rather than constantly like heroin), followed by a "down" period characterised by low energy and possible feelings of depression. Some individuals try to get over these feelings by using again. This can lead to heavy patterns of use, in turn leading to feelings of paranoia and even delusions. Stopping heavy stimulant use is often associated with severe feelings of hopelessness and depression as well as cravings to use. As the impact of stimulants reduces with regular use and is not long lasting, regular heavy use requires large amounts of money.

3. Hallucinogenic or psychedelic drugs

This is a broad category of drugs which alters perception in some way: how you see, hear, feel, smell or touch the world. This can mean that the senses get mixed up or changed. People may see colours much more brightly or hear sounds differently, or say that they can "hear" colours and "see" sounds, an experience known as synaesthesia. They might also see things that aren't there, which can be very frightening for some people. Examples include LSD, magic mushrooms, the strongest types of cannabis, and to some extent ecstasy. Only cannabis is referred to here since the other drugs are not prominent in care proceedings.

Cannabis
Cannabis is the most prevalent illegal drug in the UK and is generally used as a relaxant and mild intoxicant. The most important psychoactive ingredients are the tetrahydro-cannabinols (THC). There are suggestions that the drug can in rare cases trigger psychosis. In the UK, cannabis is

generally smoked with tobacco in a joint or "spliff", but it can also be smoked in a pipe, brewed into a drink or cooked in food.

Cannabis can lead to a state of relaxation, talkativeness and greater appreciation of sensory expectations, but can also result in confusion and psychological distress. It is regularly taken to enhance or detract from the effects of other drugs. Cannabis does not produce physical dependence. However, its use does introduce individuals to buying illegal drugs where they are more likely to come into contact with other illegal substances.

Common problems across substances

There are some common issues related to all substances. This may be because substances share a capacity to harm the developing child directly, or it may in part be attributable to the results of poverty, poor nutrition, smoking or other common factors. Features of all substance misuse during pregnancy are:

- increased risk of miscarriage;
- increased likelihood of premature birth;
- reduced birth weight;
- reduced head circumference at birth.

In addition, all substances seem linked to an increased risk of cot death – though this may in part be connected to PSM after birth. It is advisable that potential carers have an awareness of good practice in relation to cot death – such as putting babies to sleep on their back, not having babies in bed to sleep with them, correct use of mattresses, and obviously, not smoking – in order to reduce these risks. (See Sudden Infant Death resources at the end of this guide.)

In general, these conditions are themselves linked to an increased chance of poor outcomes. Thus, premature babies may have a variety of complications: low birth weight is often related to health problems and small head circumference is associated with developmental difficulties (for some children). Conversely, children born without any of these difficulties are at less risk of poor outcomes linked to maternal substance use. Indeed, many of the correlations with general developmental problems (such as attention, perceptual or behavioural difficulties) do not persist in the absence of these early indications that substance use has been problematic for the child. Level of prematurity and birth weight are therefore vital indicators of the level of problems that maternal substance misuse is likely to have caused the child.

Non-specific problems for children

There are a number of non-specific problems associated with children born to mothers who misused substances. These have more similarities than differences in relation to the various substances. This may be because many are mediated or caused in large part by social and familial factors or because different substances affect brain development in comparable ways.

Most of the non-specific issues seem to be connected to low birth weight and prematurity: they are more likely when these conditions are present, and these conditions are more common where there is substance misuse.

The most common non-specific problems include:

- lack of concentration;

- difficulty with gross or fine motor movements;

- increased likelihood of challenging behaviour.

These are all signs that tend to emerge between the ages of three and seven. However, it is generally possible to identify such issues through careful assessment by the age of two.

Associations with specific conditions

Substance misuse exposure is linked to some specific conditions that may develop in later childhood. The most important of these include statistical associations with:

- Attention Deficit Hyperactivity Disorder (ADHD); and

- alcohol or drug misuse in adolescence and adulthood.

The biggest single factor mediating these risks is the quality of the home environment: *caring homes and committed parents can make a huge difference.* Yet however good the parenting, some children will develop problems either as a result of exposure to substances in utero or because of genetic susceptibility (or a combination). It seems likely, for instance, that the probability of boys developing ADHD is doubled by PSM.

Data on the genetic inheritance of alcohol and drug problems are complicated to interpret. There is no gene for alcohol addiction. In common with a range of illnesses (such as heart disease or certain cancers) there is no single gene rsponsible. It is more likely that a variety of genes are linked to complex differences which make individuals more vulnerable. Overall, it would appear that the likelihood of boys developing an alcohol problem is approximately doubled by having a parent with one. The link does not seem as strong in girls.

SECTION I

23

Risks associated with different substances

Smoking

Cigarettes combine a variety of substances, including some with highly addictive properties and a number of poisons. Smoking during pregnancy is the most widespread form of substance misuse and the one we know most about. It is associated with an increased risk of:

- prematurity and associated health problems (which will vary between children);

- low birth weight;

- greater difficulty in keeping warm;

- risk of cot death, though this is likely to be largely or entirely due to post-natal smoking;

- heart disease in adulthood and Type 2 diabetes;

- smoking (this is reduced very greatly by not living in a smoking home).

Key practice implications:

- Information about smoking should be provided to carers and treated as seriously as other substances.

- Much of the risk from smoking is mediated by whether the child was born prematurely and with a low birth weight, so these need to be considered in evaluating future risks.

- It would appear inappropriate to place a child, whose mother smoked, in an alternative home where carers smoke, as this compounds genetic and environmental risks for serious health problems. This is rarely an issue for adoptive or foster placements, but may be an

SECTION I

under-explored area for kinship care. Detailed guidance is provided in BAAF's Practice Note 51 (2007).

Cannabis

Cannabis is usually smoked and is therefore associated with many of the risk factors for cigarettes (indeed, as cannabis smoke is not filtered, some of the harm may be greater than for smoking).

Cannabis use during pregnancy can lead to complications, as there is a reduction in the amount of oxygen nutrition delivered to the baby via the placenta. Smoking cannabis, like tobacco, can lead to a low birth weight and an increased risk of SIDS (Sudden Infant Death Syndrome). There is limited evidence on the longer-term impact on children of cannabis use in pregnancy, though some studies suggest an increase in learning and behavioural difficulties in pre-school age. It is important that information on cannabis use during pregnancy be collected if possible. It is often not focused on if more "serious" illegal drugs are being used.

Alcohol

Alcohol use is widespread in the general population and is probably the most commonly misused substance during pregnancy, with regards to children who come into care. It is also the most potentially harmful substance for children's future welfare.

The impact of alcohol use during pregnancy varies enormously. The amount consumed, the point of consumption during pregnancy and other factors, ranging from social class to the vulnerability of a specific unborn child, influence the impact of alcohol on child development. Some children born to heavy drinking women appear to have few or no symptoms. Nonetheless, overall, alcohol is associated with a range of serious, long-term problems for children.

Alcohol is teratogenic, meaning it passes through the placenta and disturbs the development and growth of the foetus. Alcohol can thus result in damage to whichever part of the foetus is currently being formed at the time of exposure, for instance the brain or developing organs or bones. The brain is vulnerable throughout the entire pregnancy, leading to permanent damage through decreased growth and abnormal connections forming between different parts of the brain, leading to abnormal thought processes and behaviour (primary disabilities). Other common physical deformities may occur in the first six weeks of pregnancy before a woman knows she is pregnant. The foetus may be small in overall size and have a small head. The damage to the central nervous system can cause difficulties in the following areas:

- intellectual disability, lowered IQ
- memory disorders
- learning disabilities
- attention disorders
- sensitivity to sights, sounds and touch
- speech and language difficulties
- mood disorders
- behavioural disorders
- autistic-like behaviours
- sleep disorders

Box 2 provides basic information on some of the key syndromes and conditions associated with alcohol misuse. The number of associated conditions, collectively termed "Foetal Alcohol Spectrum Disorders" (FASD), is somewhat confusing. It is important to note that these are not on a spectrum with "full" Foetal Alcohol Syndrome (FAS) at one end and other less significant conditions lower down. In fact, FAS involves some specific elements (such as facial features) that may not be present in children who have more significant behavioural problems or developmental delay. These are therefore a collection of conditions, each of which includes a spectrum of severity, rather than a "spectrum" from more to less serious. It seems possible that, as research progresses, further conditions will be identified.

Foetal Alcohol Spectrum Disorders (FASD)

BOX 2

SECTION I

Foetal Alcohol Syndrome (FAS)	**Physical symptoms**
	Facial features: the "face" of FAS has short eye openings (palpebral fissures), low nasal bridge, a smooth, wide philtrum (vertical groove between the middle of the upper lip and the nose) and a thin upper lip. These features are more apparent from the ages of two to ten, than at birth or in adolescence.
	Growth deficiency: small and underweight for their age often till puberty, with a small head circumference (microcephalic) at birth.
	Neurological symptoms
	Impaired fine motor skills
	Poor tandem gait

SECTION I

Partial Foetal Alcohol Syndrome (pFAS)	A diagnosis given where the child displays some but not all characteristics of FAS. Those with FAS will have confirmed Parental Alcohol Exposure (PAE) and a complex pattern of cognitive or behavioural irregular development that cannot be attributed to genetic or environmental factors.
Alcohol Related Neurodevelopmental Disorder (ARND)	**Cognitive and functional impairments are present, not unique to PAE, so for an ARND diagnosis to be confirmed PAE is required.** Effects include: Decreased head size at birth Structural brain abnormalities Attention deficits Behavioural disorders Obsessive compulsive disorder

Alcohol Related Birth Defect (ARBD)	**For diagnosis, one or more congenital defects will be present. For example:** Dysplasia of the heart Sight/hearing defects Skeletal defects Renal defects
Foetal Alcohol Effects (FAE)	**Symptoms not usually visible** Although they may not exhibit many of the physical characteristics of FAS, those with FAE will have a number of developmental delays and complications such as: Behavioural disorders Attention deficits Motor skills dysfunction Learning disabilities

SECTION I

FAS and related syndromes are found in almost one per cent of all children in the USA, making them more common than autistic spectrum disorders. There are no accurate figures for the UK, but alcohol-related harm is undoubtedly a substantial problem in the general child population. It is especially common in children who enter care, though there are no reliable figures on the extent.

FAS is the only diagnosis that is an officially sanctioned "syndrome". It requires identification of the following:

1. facial features (i.e. smooth philtrum, thin upper lip and reduced eye width), most apparent in younger children;

2. growth retardation (height or weight in the bottom 10 per cent of the population);

3. central nervous system damage;

4. prenatal alcohol exposure confirmed or unknown (for instance, for an adopted child).

Partial FAS may be diagnosed when some elements of the Syndrome (particularly 2 and 3) are present but there are not facial features, and it is not possible to confirm alcohol use during pregnancy.

A very helpful guide to looking after a child with FAS and related conditions has been produced by the British Columbia government and is available from the FAS Aware website (FASAware, 2011). An edited list of potential behaviours at different ages is reproduced from this source in Box 3.

BOX 3

Foetal Alcohol Syndrome and related conditions: typical problems experienced by children
(adapted from FASAware, 2011)

Infancy

- often tremulous and irritable, may cry a lot

- weak sucking reflex and muscle tone

- highly susceptible to illness

- feeding difficulties: often disinterested in food, feeding can take hours

- erratic sleep patterns; no predictable sleep-awake cycle

- sensitive to sights, sounds and touch

- failure to thrive

- slow to master developmental milestones (e.g. walking, talking, imitating sounds)

- problems with bonding

Preschool

- disinterest in food and disrupted sleep continue

- poor motor co-ordination

- more interested in people than objects

- overly friendly, highly social; indiscriminate with relationships

- expressive speech may be delayed

- difficulty in comprehending danger

- prone to temper tantrums and non-compliance

- short attention span

- does not respond well to changes; prefers routines

Early school

- reading and writing skills during the first two years may not be noticeably delayed

- arithmetic may be more of a problem than spelling and reading

- attention deficits and poor impulse control become more apparent as the demands for classroom attention increase

- requires constant reminders for basic activities at home and school

Later junior school

- gross motor control problems (e.g. clumsy)

- fine motor problems (e.g. trouble with handwriting, buttons, zippers, shoe laces, etc.)

- difficulties with social skills and interpersonal relationships

- poor peer relations and social isolation may be noted

- memory deficits

- exists in the "here and now," seems to lack an internal time clock

- unable to monitor his/her own work or pace him/herself

- sleep disturbances continue

- delayed physical and cognitive development

- usually a very concrete thinker, may have trouble working with ideas

- good verbal skills, superficially friendly social manner and good intentions can mask the seriousness of the problem

Adolescence

- increased truancy, school refusals and school dropouts

- reading comprehension is poorer than word recognition

- poor memory, poor abstract thinking and difficulty with basic problem solving

- often misjudged as being lazy, stubborn and unwilling to learn

- impulsive, lack of inhibition and easily influenced, subject to peer manipulation and exploitation

- difficulty showing remorse or taking responsibility for actions

- frequently behaves in ways that place him/herself or others at risk

- risk of problems with the law and involvement in the criminal justice system

- problems managing time and money

- difficulty identifying and labelling feelings

- low self-esteem

SECTION I

Brocklesby *et al* (2009, p 1)) summarised a rather concerning picture in the following way:

[Children who have suffered alcohol-related harm during pregnancy] find it difficult to process information, to make judgements and to link actions to consequences. They can suffer from hyperactivity,

*impulsiveness, short memory spans, concentration
difficulties, poor planning and organisational skills,
motor difficulties, perceptual problems and specific
learning difficulties. As they grow older, they can
have social difficulties in relating to their peer
group and often face a traumatic path through
adolescence and beyond.*

In some respects, FAS is the most straightforward of these
syndromes when planning for adoption and foster care. It can and
should usually be identified prior to any long-term placement.
More challenging are issues around other effects related to alcohol
use, which may not be identified until significant problems emerge
at a later point.

It is worth noting here that while these syndromes are disabilities
that cannot be "cured" through good quality care, there is a
strong link between the quality of the home environment and the
outcomes for these children as they grow up. In particular, some
of the findings suggest that the substantial proportion of FAS
children entering prison or having serious problems in adulthood
was very much linked to whether they remained at home or not.
The largest study of outcomes for these children found that those
who remained with their birth parents were five times more likely
to have negative outcomes than children in alternative care.

Heroin and methadone

Heroin is one of the most commonly used substances among
parents whose children come into care. Heroin is rarely used
on its own. It is usually mixed with other substances, and many
individuals will also be using methadone (a prescribed replacement
drug) or other alternatives.

The most obvious immediate effect of heroin or methadone is

that the baby is born addicted and suffers withdrawal symptoms (Neonatal Abstinence Syndrome). There does not seem to be a consistent link between the pattern of heroin use and the extent of withdrawal symptoms in the baby. The child will often be born premature and small and will therefore be particularly vulnerable. Most go into a special care unit for some days or weeks.

BOX 4

SECTION I

Neonatal Abstinence Syndrome (NAS)

NAS occurs where an infant has been prenatally exposed to substances which they have become physically dependent on, such as opiates (heroin, methadone, codeine) and amphetamines. Symptoms of withdrawal generally occur one to three days after birth; sometimes they are not visible until ten days plus of life. Known as 'Delayed Onset NAS', this can cause extra stress to the carers before diagnosis. The nature of the drug(s) taken, amount used and length of exposure will affect the symptoms exhibited, which may include: blotchy skin colouring; excessive, often high-pitched crying; seizures and irritability. Gently rocking the baby or swaddling it can help to encourage calmness.

The severity of the child's condition will dictate their treatment plan. NAS can last from one week to six months. Left untreated, the risk of fatality from the syndrome is up to 20 per cent. Babies born pre-term may not exhibit symptoms as severe as those born full term as they have not had as much exposure to substances. However, premature babies have other health risks. As part of the treatment for NAS, a doctor may prescribe a similar drug to wean the infant off the drug, and help relieve some of the withdrawal symptoms. Babies may also need a higher calorie feed to provide more nutrition; smaller and more frequent feeds can be beneficial. Long-term health risks to the infant include problems with vision such as squints.

Current research suggests that cocaine usage during pregnancy does not lead to NAS (that is, provision of more cocaine would not reduce symptoms). However, it can result in similar symptoms to those found in NAS due to blood vessels being constricted. The treatment and response – to some extent medical, but more particularly in terms of care required – are similar to those for a child experiencing NAS.

Children who have experienced NAS require particularly patient care for weeks and months afterwards. They can be "jittery", difficult to comfort and feed, and delayed in general progress.

There is little evidence that NAS is associated with any long-term conditions, though there may be a link to some sight problems. There is little doubt that taking heroin is not a good idea during pregnancy, exacerbated by the fact that it is so often impure or of variable strength. But in general terms, heroin has similarities to chemicals produced in the body and the placenta provides a higher degree of protection than it does for alcohol or cigarette smoke. It is possible that methadone used during pregnancy may lead to more severe NAS than heroin. Some other heroin substitutes are linked to neurological problems in animals and should not usually be prescribed during pregnancy.

In the period around the birth, a particularly common issue for those using illegal drugs is the risk of blood-borne viruses, such as HIV and hepatitis (particularly hepatitis C). Further information on these conditions is provided in Box 5.

BOX 5

Blood-borne viruses: hepatitis and HIV

Injecting drug users are at risk of acquiring hepatitis B and C and HIV through sharing of contaminated injecting equipment. Hepatitis B and C are viruses transmitted through blood, and in the long term they can cause serious disease of the liver. Human immunodeficiency virus (HIV) is a blood-borne infection that can compromise the immune system and lead to acquired immune deficiency syndrome (AIDS). Of these three viruses, hepatitis B is the most and HIV the least infectious.

Hepatitis B is a virus that causes inflammation of the liver which in the long term can lead to scarring of the liver (cirrhosis) and increased risk of liver cancer. Hepatitis B is transmitted through contact with blood or other body fluids contaminated with blood. Adults most commonly become infected through unprotected sexual intercourse and intravenous drug use, putting mothers who misuse alcohol and those who inject drugs at high risk. It is unusual for the virus to cross the placenta during pregnancy but the risk of transmission of hepatitis B from mother to child at delivery is 20 to 90 per cent. However, when a mother is known to be hepatitis B positive, starting the newborn baby on a course of immunisation against hepatitis B will usually prevent infection.

Hepatitis C is a virus that causes inflammation of the liver. Although most infected people will have only mild liver damage, a small minority develop serious liver damage over 20 to 30 years. Hepatitis C is transmitted through contact with blood. Most of those with the condition in the UK are injecting drug users, though it can be sexually transmitted. It is relatively rare for a baby to be infected even if their mother has hepatitis C (c.5% risk).

HIV is a viral infection that can cause acquired immune deficiency (AIDs). It can be transmitted through blood, sexual intercourse or breastfeeding. HIV can be transmitted from mother to child during pregnancy, at delivery or through breastfeeding. Without treatment this risk is approximately 25 per cent; with a combination of drug treatment and caesarean section the risk reduces to less than one per cent.

Testing for hepatitis and HIV in children

There is a separate test for each of these three viruses. Diagnosis in children under 18 months of age is complicated by the presence of maternal antibodies, which are passed to the child through the placenta but which do not necessarily indicate that the child is infected. The PCR (Polymerase Chain Reaction) test which detects the presence of a virus in the blood can assist diagnosis in children under 18 months of age. Additionally, it is important to understand that it can take up to three to six months from the time of infection until the tests become positive, so testing may have to be repeated if initially negative.

Treatment

Hepatitis and HIV are chronic conditions which often require no initial treatment. Treatment has improved considerably in recent years, especially for hepatitis B and HIV, so early diagnosis is very important. Regular monitoring should be carried out so that if treatment is needed, it can be initiated as soon as possible for the best outcomes.

Cocaine (including crack cocaine)

Cocaine is a crystallised powder derived from the coca plant. Crack cocaine is a form of cocaine that provides a more intense and shorter "high". Many users find this highly psychologically addictive and can develop substantial crack habits. Crack misuse is far more common in the parents of children who come into care than the use of powdered cocaine. In the period after birth, babies exposed to cocaine exhibit many of the symptoms associated with NAS, though this is caused by restriction of the blood vessels rather than withdrawal (see Box 4).

During the 1990s there was widespread concern that the children of crack-misusing parents appeared to have serious behavioural difficulties and attention and learning problems at pre-school ages. Later research, which looked at children who had been born to crack-using mothers but who did not live at home, found little evidence to support the existence of such difficulties. It seems likely that the severe problems identified were related to the very poor care and home situations and serious poverty being experienced by these children.

Amphetamines

Commonly known by street names such as "speed" or "whizz", amphetamine is a stimulant that can be snorted or taken intravenously. There are strong grounds for believing that amphetamine use is likely to affect the development of babies. Its use is linked to reductions in blood flow to the placenta, with persistent use related to reduction in appetite and therefore poor nutrition. There are many studies identifying potential problems that may be related to amphetamine use, including heart defects, cleft palate and intestinal abnormalities. Although these studies have been too small to yield unequivocal results, there does appear to be a link to reduced birth weight and increased risk of premature birth or miscarriage. Sustained use seems to produce withdrawal symptoms that include jitteriness, drowsiness and respiratory problems in newborns. These require expert medical intervention.

CHAPTER 3

Implications for carers and professionals

This chapter makes a variety of suggestions for prospective parents and professionals about identifying and dealing with potential issues in relation to children whose parents misused substances.

Assessment and information

Accurate assessment of a child's needs and early identification of potential problems is a crucial step in considering whether a family will likely be able to meet the child's needs. It is also vital to monitor the development of any problems after a child has been placed, to ensure that families and professionals can provide the best possible response as early as possible.

Assessment requires:

- As much information as possible about maternal drinking and drug-taking in pregnancy (this should

certainly include cigarettes and alcohol use).
Unfortunately it is often very difficult to obtain an
accurate account.

- Information about the birth and early development of
the child, which is important in understanding the
potential impact of maternal substance misuse during
pregnancy. It is particularly important to know whether
the child was born prematurely (and if so by how long)
and what their birth weight and length were. (These
are generally expressed as "percentiles", i.e. how they
compare to the general population.)

- As much information as possible about the wider family,
for instance, is there a familial pattern of alcohol or
drug misuse?

- Most essentially, a thorough and comprehensive
assessment of the child's current progress across all
areas of their development. This provides the best
evidence in relation to the emergence of any particular
problem at a comparatively early stage.

Living with uncertainty

Even if the assessments are all comparatively positive, caring for
a child subjected to maternal substance misuse creates a degree
of uncertainty about their future progress. Of course, there is
always uncertainty about how a child will develop, but this is much
higher when there are substantial genetic or other risk factors. In
deciding whether to take on a specific child, it may be helpful to
think about the range of possible outcomes; it is also important to
be able to live with the uncertainty.

It is particularly difficult to know what the prognosis is for very
young children. In general terms, younger children are more likely
to have good outcomes: they will have been exposed to less abuse
and neglect and may have fewer attachment-related problems. On

the other hand, many of the difficulties identified in Chapter 2 are hard or impossible to identify in children under two years. This creates a dilemma for prospective carers and each family will need to make its own decisions about the degree of uncertainty it can live with. This question is more pronounced for adopters or foster carers, but it is there for all parents. Children may be born with or develop difficulties at any stage, and being able to live with some of that uncertainty is part of the "job description" for parents.

Deciding whether a child and family are the right "fit"

One of the best resources is likely to be the specialist medical adviser for the adoption and fostering agency. They should have had sight of all relevant documentation, as well as the opportunity to assess the child. Potential carers should have a chance to consult them about the nature of any particular issues affecting a child and the likely prognosis.

For adopters, meeting current foster carers and having an in-depth discussion about the child can also be enormously helpful in identifying potential problems or difficulties as well as for gathering information about the child's strengths and the rewards in caring for them.

Children born to mothers who misused drugs should be followed up by specialist paediatricians for two years. Services in relation to alcohol misuse tend to be more variable. It is nearly always advisable to talk to a specialist, especially when a child is seriously being considered as a match.

It is always acceptable to say that a child is not the right match for you and your family. Never feel guilty or bad about it: it is much better to be honest with yourself about what you can and cannot cope with. Never let yourself feel pressurised into a match. Just because social workers feel you are right for a child, does not mean you have to agree. After all, you will be looking after this child in the long term. Do think about the future, not just the present. What would being this child's parent be like not just now but in 5, 10, 15 or even 20 years?

Having gathered together all the available information, it is worth thinking through some "worst case scenarios": if this child has currently hidden problems, how will you cope? Your social worker should be there to have discussions like this with you.

Working to help the child

As has been repeatedly stated, the most important single factor associated with improving outcomes for children is a caring and committed family. The brain is very "plastic" – it develops throughout childhood and into adulthood. There is a lot of potential for problems experienced at one stage to be overcome or reduced through good nurture as the child grows older.

This means that for the majority of children who have relatively minor issues, responsive and stimulating parenting and firm boundaries are likely to significantly improve problems around behaviour and attention. Even if children have permanent disabilities related to alcohol or other substance misuse, good parenting remains the best route for ameliorating the extent of the problems associated with their disability.

Support services

When there are issues, and particularly if they are serious, it is extremely important that the adoption support plan or the fostering agreement reflect this. Before a child is placed, the carer is in a strong position to negotiate an appropriate plan. If you feel that a child has serious problems and caring for them in the long term will be challenging, it is worth discussing with the local authority what support would be available. This might include:

- provision of an adoption or fostering allowance to cover additional expenses;

- provision of respite care (the most common service requested by families whose children have FAS);

- detailed plans for other services that may support the family, such as therapeutic interventions and specialist educational support.

Late onset problem behaviours including alcohol or drug use

One of the problems for adopted children whose parents misused substances is that they are at increased risk of developing challenging or anti-social behaviour in adolescence, including misuse of drugs or alcohol. The reason for this may in part be genetic or it may be related to exposure to substances in utero. In general, research has far more to say about the development of such problems than what works in preventing potential difficulties from becoming actual problems, but the following are some general prescriptions.

- The best protector against the development of problems involves a combination of care and appropriate discipline – sometimes called authoritative parenting. Providing clear boundaries and being consistent in enforcing them may be particularly important for children whose parents misused substances.

- For most children adolescence is a challenging time as they move towards adulthood and often come into conflict with those around them. For some adopted children this can be exacerbated by the fact that they are adopted or by past experiences. Maintaining open lines of communication is very important.

● Behaviours that may be linked to poor outcomes can also help children to succeed. There is some evidence that children of alcoholic parents can be high achievers. It is hypothesised that this may be because they are more prepared to take risks and are more sociable than other children. Think about how characteristics that might be problematic in one context could help a child succeed in another. For instance, would your child shine in team sports, adventure scouting or martial arts? Each child is different, but it is worth finding positive ways of channelling unusual energy.

● Parents should always be open with children about why they are adopted. How much it is appropriate to tell a child, and when, will depend on age and stage of understanding. Probably before adolescence it would usually be helpful to let a child know that their mother or father had a problem in controlling the amount they drank or the drugs they took. At the same time, it would be worth starting discussions with children about alcohol and drugs, in an open way. The most important thing is to keep the channels of communication open so that children can make informed decisions as they move into adulthood.

● Early use of cigarettes or alcohol is a key risk factor for developing subsequent problems and should be taken seriously as warning signs.

Concluding comment

The above suggestions are intended to be helpful for carers and professionals. They cannot cover every eventuality, and in some circumstances, specialist professional input may be required.

It is worth repeating a point made in the introduction. As far as we can tell, outcomes for children whose parents have misused alcohol or drugs are overall no worse than for adopted children who do not have this legacy. The above list of potential symptoms should not lead to the erroneous conclusion that most of these children will have serious problems.

Nonetheless, many of them will have problems at some stage – and a few will have serious problems. The two case studies that follow explore what it is like to live with and care for children who struggle with the effects of parental drug or alcohol misuse.

SECTION I

47

PARENTING CHILDREN AFFECTED BY PARENTAL SUBSTANCE MISUSE

DONALD FORRESTER WITH SALLY BAKER
AND JANE HARTLEY

Introduction

If one creates an imaginary spectrum of level of difficulty, both of the following stories are very much at the more serious end of that spectrum: they describe caring for multiple children with mild to serious disabilities, often with limited professional support. They can help us to think about the more challenging issues that may affect children, but it should not be concluded that adopting a child whose parents misused drugs or alcohol will necessarily involve this level of difficulty. It is hoped that these accounts will help prospective carers to evaluate the level they feel able to cope with.

These two stories were obtained through BAAF's links with a range of adoptive parents. Despite being produced independently of the previous section, they feature many of the issues discussed:

- profound difficulties can be associated with FASD and with obtaining an accurate diagnosis of the symptoms;

- the crucial importance of premature birth and low birth weight, and the possible harm caused to children (both a potential problem in its own right and often an indication of more serious drug or alcohol use during pregnancy);

- the importance of accurate professional assessment of children's needs at an early stage.

While the stories were not written for this purpose, they clearly indicate the huge difference loving and patient parents can make. These children were born with some serious hurdles to overcome – 'bruised before birth' as a previous BAAF publication termed it. The most extraordinary feature of the stories is the exceptional quality of the parenting that these children subsequently experienced. So, these accounts don't simply illustrate the research findings in Section 1: they show what an extraordinary difference adoption can make to children, even when those children come with serious problems.

SECTION II

Foetal Alcohol Syndrome?

Sally Baker and her husband have adopted three full siblings, Hamish, Sophie and Emily, all of whom were premature with very low birth weight. Both birth parents had been misusing drugs, alcohol and tobacco but despite the obvious symptoms – including various disabilities – several years on, none of the children have ever been diagnosed with FASD.

Our story

We always imagined having at least three or four children. I come from a very small family and was often envious of my husband's large family.

We initially approached a local authority with our wish to adopt, only to be told that we were too old for a young child (we were in our mid-30s). We eventually got

53

taken on by a private adoption agency. The home study, with a part-time social worker, took almost 18 months but it was worth it. Yes, we had to answer sensitive questions but we could always see the reason why, so it never felt intrusive.

We were prepared to take on children with physical disabilities but felt we would not be able to deal with a life-limiting illness. We wanted a sibling group in order to complete our family in one go and thought it would be good for the children to be able to stay together. Although we had been to preparation groups and training, knowledge about developmental trauma was still very limited at the time.

We were eventually approved to adopt two children up to the age of seven and expected to have a school-age child and maybe a slightly younger sibling. We were approved in June, and in August our social worker told us about a brother and sister aged 16 and eight months. We were excited by the thought of having two such young children but had to wait till January before the children came to us as there were serious health concerns over our daughter-to-be who had been born extremely prematurely.

Pre-adoption thoughts about alcohol misuse

We had been told that both birth parents had been misusing drugs and alcohol and cigarettes but the exact extent of it was not known. We understood that because of the young age of the children and our daughter's extreme prematurity there might be problems in the future, but at that stage no symptoms of Foetal Alcohol Syndrome (FAS) had been noted; the children showed no physical signs of a disability and we were not worried.

SECTION II

We knew that the younger the child was permanently placed with a family, the greater the possibility of recovery and hoped that nurture could win over nature.

We knew from our social worker and from reading children's profiles in *Be My Parent* and *Children Who Wait* that a lot of birth families abused drugs and alcohol, and we had a basic knowledge about the effect substance misuse might have on children.

We understood that alcohol can be more dangerous to a foetus than cocaine or heroin as it passes through the placenta, and can permanently kill off nerve endings and connections between brain cells.

The impact depends on the amount of alcohol and the stage of pregnancy when it was consumed; for example, heavy drinking during the first three months can lead to physical deformities (misshapen ears, short-sightedness, small eyes) as the baby's face is forming.

The fact that it is possible to have Foetal Alcohol Spectrum Disorders (FASD) without the facial characteristics – if the mother did not drink during the period when the mid-face was forming – means that only a limited number of children and adults with FASD get diagnosed. This can cause problems in the future, as high expectations placed on people with FASD put them under pressure and leave them unable to cope, which, in turn, can lead to re-traumatisation and the emergence of serious secondary disabilities, such as depression. FASD conditions are life-long conditions and adults may find themselves having difficulty holding down a job or forming relationships.

SECTION II

The sad thing about FASD and any related disorders is that they are entirely preventable.

Our children's story

Our adopted children Hamish, Sophie and Emily, are full siblings. They have two more brothers, who also live with adoptive families, and we meet with one of them regularly. All three of our children were premature (31, 24 and 34 weeks), though, according to birth mum, this is genetic and runs in her family. However, it is widely known that excessive drinking during pregnancy is harmful and can result in pre-term delivery and decreased birth weight.

All our children had a very low birth weight: Hamish weighed 1,800gms and was considered small even for his premature delivery. He stayed one month in special care. Sophie weighed merely 720gms and spent almost 17 weeks in hospital. There had been only a 50:50 chance that she would live. Even after she was in foster care, she stopped breathing several times. Emily was the "biggest" and weighed 2.21kg; she had also had the longest gestation at 34 weeks. All children had been removed at birth and gone into foster care. However, there was some contact with birth mum and dad, if and when they attended.

Hamish spent 20 months in foster care and had had three foster placements and one stay in a mother and baby unit before he came to us. Multiple placements can lead to attachment problems and a sense of not belonging, as early bonding is disrupted by frequent changes of the carer.

The girls were "luckier" and had only been with one

foster carer. The first time we set eyes on Hamish and Sophie, we were amazed by how tiny Sophie was. Until she was about seven years old she was always smaller than her peers. When she started walking, people were amazed to see such a tiny child on her feet so early. Hamish was a bit of a bruiser and grew to be larger than average. Sadly, this didn't do him any favours, as everybody mistook him for an older child and expected more of him. Already when we first met him, we noticed that he was very unsteady on his legs and yet it took another year to have him diagnosed with Hemiplegia (a partial paralysis affecting one side of the body). When he came to us, he did not know how to play and had very limited speech. Our concerns were ignored or dismissed as he was "just lazy" or a "typical boy", slow to learn. We eventually managed to get him speech therapy, which paid off: it is now hard to get a word in! He was a very happy child but used to dribble at an awful rate. He was also very late potty training and we still have issues with bedwetting and soiling today, which apparently is not uncommon in children with FAS.

The first few weeks seemed to go by in a flash and it was exhausting looking after two such young children. Hamish had not been taught to feed himself and Sophie had not been put on solids, so there I was, with one each side of me, handing a spoonful to each in turn. Luckily Hamish was a good eater. Sophie was fussier and stayed on her bottles for a very long time. As she was so tiny she had to have lots of additional supplements and special injections for her respiratory system.

I survived with the help of a playpen, in which I could put one child while I was attending to the

*other's needs, especially when Sophie was having
one of her full-blown tantrums.*

We were also very fortunate that our children loved
their naps and carried on having them till they started
nursery school. This was my lifesaver since all our
family lived far away and I only had my husband to
give me a break. Taking them to any playgroup was
next to impossible, as Sophie would never sit and was
considered disruptive, whereas Hamish would often
cry. We eventually found a small church playgroup that
was very welcoming; the church has been a great help
in making us feel like a "normal" family by accepting the
children as they are.

In the first couple of years Hamish used to have a lot
of crying fits and I would sit with him, holding him and
trying to calm him. Because of the small age gap the
children were very competitive with each other and
fought for my attention. It was hard to see to their
individual needs and, in hindsight, I sometimes wonder
if they would have been better off placed separately as
only children. That way they would have got maximum
attention and stimulation. However, we can only do our
best and hope that it is enough. Hamish would often
complain that we preferred Sophie since she needed so
much attention when she was little and not very well,
and when she had one of her emotional meltdowns.

When the children were five and four, we heard about
a paediatrician who specialised in adopted children and
managed to have Hamish and Sophie seen by her. Both
children subsequently received diagnoses of Attention
Deficit Hyperactivity Disorder (ADHD), and Hamish was
also diagnosed with Aspergers syndrome (a condition

on the autistic spectrum). At five years old he had social communication problems, poor eye contact and limited play skills. This explains why he disliked noisy playgroups and used to hide behind me or under the table crying. More recently, we discovered that he has mild dyslexia, which is why he has difficulties with spelling.

There is still a debate whether Sophie actually has ADHD or Attachment Disorder, as the symptoms for both are very similar.

When the children were diagnosed with ADHD, the first thing we were offered was Ritalin, a drug we refused, as we felt behaviour management might be a safer route to helping children already affected by substance misuse.

Sophie always had problems separating from me and still does not like it when I go out in the evening. Unfortunately this paediatrician has now left and it is very hard to find the right expert and access financial support. We would like to get an appointment at the Maudsley (a centre for behavioural therapy) as the children's behaviours are getting more challenging, but have already been told there is no funding due to the cuts.

Despite her extreme prematurity, Sophie does not have any physical disabilities. However, she had sensory integration issues, which have persisted to this day: she cannot wear some clothes as a lot of fabrics irritate her. Sensory integration dysfunction can also be linked to foetal alcohol disorders.

Sophie was an incredibly active child and could never

SECTION II

59

sit still or concentrate. Not having any other children, we simply assumed this was normal, although we found it extremely exhausting. It was only when we spoke to friends or observed other children in a restaurant or park that we realised that some children can actually sit through a meal. Sophie also has spectacular temper tantrums when things don't go her way, a behaviour which is emotionally more compatible with a two- to three-year-old and exemplifies the discrepancy between her emotional and her chronological age. As a baby she used to scream; now, aged 10, it is more verbal abuse, throwing, breaking things and door slamming.

We have found out that hyperactivity, attention deficits, problems with sustained and focused attention, irritability and immature social behaviour as well as lack of control over emotions are all characteristics of FAS.

Shortly after we had Hamish and Sophie, we had the opportunity to meet with their birth mum, which we thought would be helpful: she would not just be a name and we would be able to tell the children more about her as an actual person. It was a bit awkward as she still thought the children would be coming back to her later on. But we had brought a list of questions and she was willing to answer them. We have annual letterbox contact and while Hamish is not at all interested in his birth family, Sophie gets very anxious around letterbox time, and often feels angry that she cannot see her birth mum until she is 18.

Four years after we had had Hamish and Sophie, we were contacted by social services to tell us that the children had a little sister: would we be interested in giving her a home as well? Since things had calmed down a bit and Hamish and Sophie seemed quite settled, we felt ready to take on one more child. Until Emily arrived, FAS had not really featured greatly in our thoughts. Yes, the other two had various problems but we, as well as the professionals who had seen the children, failed to associate them with FAS/FASD (Foetal Alcohol Spectrum Disorders).

Emily has the same birth parents but apparently mum had been exposed to more alcohol misuse during this pregnancy, although it seemed impossible to get more precise information. Emily was 15 months when she came to us and initially appeared very different from the other two. She seemed less hyper than Sophie, was able to play and made great eye contact. She settled in well and we considered ourselves lucky that there appeared to be no issues. However, we soon realised that she had the same tendency to fall as her brother. This time round we knew where to turn and very quickly had a diagnosis of Hemiplegia; we were offered physiotherapy, occupational therapy and a Portage worker (home pre-school tuition). We found a lovely supportive nursery and things seemed to be going great.

After a while, however, we realised that Emily appeared to have more problems with concentration than her siblings; she was even less able to sit still and had absolutely no fear of anything. Worse, she would talk to anybody and was inappropriately friendly to strangers. She also had, and still has, very immature social behaviour, difficulty learning from consequences, and lack of control over her emotions.

We tried to get her assessed by the Child and

Adolescent Mental Health Service (CAMHS), but because she was so young, they were reluctant to make a diagnosis. Emily is now six and we are still struggling to get her assessed and diagnosed. We originally suspected that she had learning difficulties like her birth parents, but some developmental tests showed that she is very intelligent and in some areas functions like an eight-year-old. We think her behaviour may be linked to foetal alcohol disorder, but as she shows no facial features, it is very difficult to get her diagnosed.

School

We were fortunate that all our children spent almost two years with us before starting nursery school. All three had been to a nursery for a couple of mornings from when they were about two-and-a-half years, so starting nursery school did not come as a huge shock. Sophie struggled a bit as she was so small and the uniform was much too big for her. She was very clingy but it helped that Hamish was with her for one term before moving up to Reception. Hamish struggled from day one as he was one of the youngest in his class but looked a lot older. He found handwriting very difficult – partly because his Hemiplegia forces him to be left-handed and we think he may otherwise have been right-handed. He also finds it hard to read and concentrate. We tried to get him assessed for a Statement of Special Educational Needs, but lost at tribunal as he was 'not failing enough'. He suffered all through his years in primary school and was bullied at least once a term. However, we were extremely proud of him when he reached an acceptable level in all subjects at the end of primary school.

He has now moved on to secondary mainstream with some support, and it is a completely new ball game.

Instead of two or three teachers he has up to 16; he has to move classrooms for every subject and for a child with executive function problems, this is a huge challenge.

The brain damage caused by pre-natal exposure to alcohol often results in neurological impairment of the executive functions, causing problems with short-term memory, organisation, abstract concepts, problem-solving and controlling impulses.

Hamish struggles with the amount of homework he gets and finds it very hard to get started on anything except playing on the computer or Wii. We have found that teachers constantly need reminding about his difficulties. The other day, his class watched a scary film clip and he was terrified for days afterwards. Another time, a teacher did not give him enough time to write down his homework tasks, so we ended up writing in his homework book that he has mild dyslexia and needs more time.

Sophie is enjoying her last year in primary school but only because she has a very supportive and understanding teacher, who even took the time to read a book about adopted children in the classroom. We have tried hard to get teachers to understand the difficulties adopted children face in the education system, but we have frequently met with a complete lack of understanding and disinterest, not only from teachers but also from a lot of officials at the local education authority. We had chosen a small local primary school as we thought the children needed to feel safe and secure, and were worried that they might get lost in a big school. Initially that was probably a good decision, but we eventually figured that it might have been better to choose a bigger school: firstly, there would have been more facilities and staff, and secondly, the jump to secondary school would not have been quite as big. At the moment there are as many children in Hamish's year as there were in his whole primary school.

It took us four years to get Sophie put on School Action (a programme of learning support planned and delivered by the school). Because she is quite able academically, her social difficulties, which mainly occur at free play, often go unnoticed, but we can always tell by her behaviour at home afterwards that she has had problems. We get tremendous tantrums and eventually, in bed at night, she might tell us the cause. On her first day in primary school I was taken aside and told that she had hit a teaching assistant and would not apologise! When I eventually got to the bottom of it, it appeared that Sophie would not eat much at lunchtime and when asked to finish her food she supposedly hit the assistant.

Sophie is aware of her difficulties and although her school has just removed her "social support needs" action point from her Individual Education Plan (IEP), she still struggles with friendships and social conventions. At the same time, she is now quite assertive and wrote on her IEP, 'I try hard to make friends but it doesn't really work' and 'I also get angry easily'. I am delighted about the level of insight she has acquired, but also feel sad that she is aware how hard it is for her to make friends. She often complains, 'Why don't they [the teachers] realise that I have special needs?' Hamish, on the other hand, despite his communication problems, always manages to make at least one friend.

We now get this denial about special needs a lot from Emily's teachers. There have been incidents of soiling in the school garden – we get occasional lapses at home too, soiling on the toilet floor – and the only reason we know about it is because her sister keeps telling us that Emily constantly gets told off. Sophie is very protective of her little sister and gets angry if the teachers don't seem to understand her. When we raised the issue at a parents' evening, we were told there were no issues!

At 10, Sophie is now at an age where she feels people should understand about her and her siblings' "problems" and not constantly tell them off because of them. Emily, now aged six, already had the label of "the naughty child" in Year 1, and some parents do not like their children playing with her. I sometimes feel like saying, 'She had a tough time when she was little and it is not her fault.' However, it is Emily's story and not up to me to interfere and disclose information. Emily struggles especially with reading and writing and is bottom of her class. Sadly, she believes that she is "rubbish'" and says that everybody is better than her. She finds concentrating in class extremely difficult and needs frequent movement breaks. She chooses to be the class clown to get attention, even though most of it is negative. Ideally she should be in a small class with a lot of one-to-one support. However, we know that we will not be able to get her a statement of special educational needs, as, like Hamish, she too is not failing enough… yet.

While Hamish does not talk much about the fact that he is adopted, Sophie loves to draw attention to herself and often talks about her birth parents, especially birth mum. One day in school she mentioned how her dad had been in prison and it sounded like she was talking about her adoptive dad. Unfortunately, she still does not understand that she needs to be selective with the information she discloses and whom she tells. Poor judgement is another aspect of FAS.

While one teacher always consulted with me before discussing a sensitive topic in class, most others forgot and a few times we had to pick up the pieces afterwards.

Discussing drugs and alcohol could be another tricky area for our children. Sophie already worries that she might become like her birth dad because of her temper tantrums, and get into trouble with the police.

I have alerted the secondary school she will soon join and hope they will remember. The bonus of a large school is that Hamish is not the only adopted child and there are children from the care system and from broken homes, so the training of secondary school teachers appears to be a little wider: they mentioned at the start that Hamish might need a nurture group. Although many of the problems our children have can be attributed to alcohol misuse, some could also be due to prematurity, and it is sometimes difficult to separate out the different strands. This is another reason why getting a diagnosis of FAS is so difficult.

Living with a disability

Because they have IEPs in school, both Hamish and Sophie are aware that they have special needs. Sophie gets annoyed when she does not get enough help in school as she really needs it, or when her sister gets told off yet again. Hamish is more oblivious. Only the other day he said to me, 'Surely I don't have a disability?' We worry for him as he is still very naïve, gullible, easily impressed and influenced. Once, when the boys' toilet was broken, the boys in his class said Hamish did it and it never occurred to him to contradict them, although he didn't do it. Another time, his friend told him that he had a million pounds in the bank and again Hamish believed it. He finds it hard to read facial expressions and sometimes gets over familiar with children he has just met. He doesn't understand how and when to back off and ends up getting hurt.

As our children look "normal" to an outsider, we sometimes get comments such as 'Can she not sit still?' or 'Is he not a bit old for this behaviour?' There are times when it would be nice to be able to go out as a family and just have fun. Unfortunately, often one of the children plays up or has a tantrum and we end up very stressed and regret having gone out. However, despite it all, we would not have it any other way. Given the history of alcohol misuse, Sophie could have been blind and deaf and possibly not even alive, and is now a great dancer and horse rider; Hamish was a poor walker and has learned to compensate. Emily is still trying to find her niche but is great at dramatics on and off the stage!

We are lucky that our local Carers' Support office has helped us fill in forms for Disability Living Allowance (DLA) and for Carer's Support. It took us a while to see ourselves as carers as well as parents; we had simply taken for granted the fact that as a parent you care for your children and ignored the fact that our level of care is over and above that of most other parents.

The DLA has been great in helping us pay for therapies for the children (physiotherapy and occupational therapy, therapeutic riding, cranial osteopathy, music therapy),

SECTION II

which we could not have afforded otherwise. However, it is quite depressing filling in the forms, as you have to focus on all the things your child cannot do, and more than once we had to go to tribunal to prove our case.

Occasionally the children feel special having a disability, like when they were invited to No. 10 for a special Christmas party and were the envy of their friends.

Promoting resilience and independence

This takes some getting used to – for us and the children. Since Hamish started secondary school, he walks with a friend; luckily it is very close to our house because he is easily distracted and crossing roads can still be a hazard. He remains very insecure and if in a shop will not go to the counter on his own but will ask me, or one of his sisters, to come with him. We hope that, with time, we will be able to build up his confidence.

Sophie is more independent, sometimes too much so for her own good, and does not always understand the dangers of the internet and Facebook in particular, or why it is not a good idea to walk through a dark alleyway at night. Because of her birth parents' history, she dislikes drunks and people who smoke, and gets quite scared when we are out in the evening and come across people who are intoxicated.

Emily has no sense of danger but we hope this will come with age. She is still very inappropriately friendly to strangers.

What and who have helped and what has not

In terms of therapies and activities,

Hamish has benefited greatly from therapeutic riding, swimming and Judo. They all helped to build his self-esteem as well as improve his posture and balance.

He could do with some more occupational and physiotherapy rather than the annual check-up.

Sophie did not require any physical help, but did benefit from occupational therapy because of her sensory integration difficulties. She was given a sensory diet and we were shown exercises to desensitise her body. She had two years of psychotherapy at CAMHS, but in our opinion it made very little difference as they did not take the adoption factor seriously enough. I was sometimes asked, 'Why does she need to talk so much about her birth mum?' and she hated going there. The sessions were one to one, whereas it would have been a lot more beneficial to have had sessions as a family, or at least together with one parent.

I feel that all the developmental and adoption training my husband and I attended empowered us to help the children and understand them better. We found *The Piece of Cake* training by Adoption UK especially useful as it went right back to our childhood, looked at prenatal aspects and developmental trauma, but also stressed that adopters need to make time for themselves, which is very important and often gets forgotten.

Emily has had a lot more therapeutic input and Portage since the Early Years team was in place by the time she needed it. We found Early Years very good: they not only helped her to develop her fine motor and play skills, but also educated us parents about how we can best

SECTION II

69

support our children.

Sophie and Hamish had a couple of years of music therapy that we paid for privately with our DLA and it helped the children to bond better. We had found the constant squabbles exhausting, and when Emily came along, felt something had to be done to help the children get along better with one another. Music therapy was non-directive and the children could express their feelings freely. Hamish especially liked banging the big drum and letting out his anger.

Most of all it has been helpful for us to talk to other parents.

As a member of our local Parent Forum, I have met a lot of parents with children with special needs and we were able to network. We used to have a toddler group just for adopted children when Sophie and Hamish arrived, and through it parents and children made very good friends. It was such a relief to come to a playgroup where nobody asked you about your pregnancy or breast-feeding. Adoption UK has also been very helpful in terms of training as well as meeting other parents.

Our social worker has always been there for us. When we had our introductions with Emily, she actually spent an afternoon with Hamish and Sophie and ever since that time, she keeps saying that she has enormous respect for us as she doesn't know how we manage them. It is good to hear that we are doing a good job and to have people understand that we are doing "therapeutic parenting" that is over and above "normal" parenting.

We are still trying to find out what lies at the bottom of

SECTION II

Emily's struggles. We suspect it is FAS, but since she does not have the facial characteristics, we may never get that diagnosis, despite the fact that she displays the same behaviours and symptoms as children who have been diagnosed with FAS.

- Trust your instinct, you know your child best.

- Don't ever stop talking with your children.

- Network with other (adoptive) parents.

- If possible, meet a birth parent and take a photo of you together and take notes.

- Pass any relevant information that might affect learning on to your child's teacher/s.

- Think emotional age not chronological age.

- Insist on full assessments if you have any concerns regarding your child's development.

- Remember you can have the symptoms of FAS without the features.

- Dislike the behaviour not the child.

Parenting the children of drug users

*Jane and Neal Hartley have three adopted children –
twins Christopher and Thomas, and Richard who joined
the family later at 12 months old. All had the same
birth mother but two different fathers, and each was
born with drug-withdrawal symptoms. Jane and Neal
also have two birth children of their own.*

Our story

Our current family household of seven is much larger
than the "adopt one and have a birth child" nuclear
family of four that we imagined we would have.

We chose to adopt and then try for our own for a
number of reasons. Firstly, a few of our friends had
discussed adoption but plans faded once the reality of
having birth children took over. We realised this change

of heart could come to us too. Secondly, we did know that there were potential fertility issues and didn't want to "waste" our (slightly) more youthful parenting years failing to get pregnant. Thirdly, we knew that many adoptions fail and that for many families, the adopted children's needs come second to the birth children's. We wanted our adopted children to have priority right from the beginning. Lastly and possibly most important to us, we felt that if we failed to have a birth child we might be less devastated if we already had a thriving adoptive family.

Eventually, NCH (then National Children's Home, now Action for Children) took us on and assessed us over a period of seven months for two children up to the age of seven. We felt we could only take on children who would become independently mobile and didn't have a life-limiting illness. I knew I would not have the patience to manage an autistic child and was slightly embarrassed but realistic about admitting I would struggle with one who was diabetic or had a severe facial disfigurement. We felt we wanted a sibling pair because we found it difficult to think of a child being separated from everything that they knew and found familiar. We also thought it might be a shorter wait for us. We had hoped to have a school-age child and a younger child, thinking that would make it easier to give them individual time. While I liked looking after newborn babies at work, and they definitely gave me clucky feelings, I also felt that they were essentially a bit boring and wasn't quite sure what I would do all day at home.

Pre-adoption thoughts about substance misuse
We thought a bit about children who were "drug babies" and investigated further. Anecdotally, it seemed that these

were the youngest children available. We felt we would prefer a child of at least a year to 18 months because we reckoned by then they would have "declared" a number of hints of potential problems to come. We were fairly reassured by the Toronto Adoption Study, which seemed to show that nurture definitely won out over nature for most of these children. The evidence seemed to be telling us that they might be a bit scatty and disorganised, might have "fringe special needs", but that the vast majority went to mainstream school either with or without additional support. This was the flavour of information from the local health visitor too. However, the nurture aspect could be damaged if children had lots of moves in foster care.

The children's story

Our adopted children, Thomas, Christopher and Richard, all have, or had, drug-misusing birth parents. All three have the same birth mother and they have two different fathers. They also have an older brother, Daniel, who lives with their maternal grandmother.

Thomas and Christopher, our twins, were also born ten weeks early after an emergency caesarean section when the placenta became detached.

We were told it is common for drug misusers to have more complicated pregnancies and to have premature babies.

Christopher was ventilated for a few days after birth and also had some seizures related to drug withdrawal. Both babies stayed in hospital for six weeks to manage their drug withdrawal symptoms.

There is a range of drug withdrawal symptoms in newborn babies and it seemed our adopted babies experienced them all. The special baby care unit has charts that score the severity of withdrawal. Oddly, it seemed to us, babies whose mothers have been on methadone have a longer and more drawn-out experience of withdrawal compared to those with mothers on heroin, who withdraw much more abruptly and often more painfully. At the severe end, babies can have all kinds of seizures or fits (like Christopher). Sometimes these can cluster and they have to be put on a drip of continuous anti-seizure medication for a few days. More often, they have a few short seizures and are very jumpy and excessively alert. These babies are put on oral anti-seizure medication until their symptoms have settled. This might take a few days or months. If they only have one or two seizures and they last less than five minutes, then they are often just kept under observation. We understood that these seizures do not increase the risk of later epilepsy unless something else is found wrong, like a brain deformity. Other symptoms of drug withdrawal include shrill crying and a poor sleep pattern. This may be particularly bad in the first month.

Babies can remain extremely unsettled even when awake and be difficult to soothe. They may be sick more often in the sense of bringing up their milk, but I think this is because they are crying so much rather than because there is anything wrong with their stomachs. Again, this is usually in the early weeks.

Our social worker explained that most mothers will not declare all of their drug use, and that some hospitals routinely screen the mother's urine for drugs at the time of birth, but that information wasn't available in the hospital where the boys were born.

There are some milder symptoms of withdrawal, which don't seem to cause the babies any especial distress, such as frequent sneezing. The main concern for our twins was that one of them had the fits; they both had the sneezing and were very irritable and slow to establish a feeding and sleeping routine. (Apparently, special care units usually only deem babies with withdrawal symptoms ready for discharge once they have achieved a four-hourly feeding pattern, as they consider three-hourly feeds through the night to be too frequent for the well-being of new mums.) Premature babies don't usually get a sucking reflex until 32 weeks gestation, so our boys did well to be discharged at 34 weeks gestation, that is, six weeks before they were due to be born.

Their parents did visit a few times while the twins were in hospital, but frequently forgot to come. They bought them each a tiny teddy bear, small enough to sit in an egg cup. The babies went straight from hospital into foster care. Two other family members came forward to be assessed as long-term kin carers but were deemed unsuitable. The children languished in care for two-and-a-half years before being placed with us.

We were told that Christopher had a mild spastic diplegia. This meant that the muscles were always a bit tense on his inner thighs. When you picked him up, instead of his legs hanging straight down, the left ankle would cross the right and the right cross the left. They called this "scissoring". The other effect was that his Achilles tendons (the bit on the back of the heel) was tight so he couldn't put his feet flat on the floor because the tendons were too short, so he ended up walking on his toes. Christopher could walk with special boots and Thomas had a "bit of speech delay". Of course we fell instantly in love with them on seeing their pictures in Adoption UK and *Be My Parent* (photo listing journals for children needing families). When we had passed the various hurdles and first received a video of them, it was abundantly clear that they were functioning as babies: being fed from a single spoon and bowl in high chairs; Christopher was painfully thin and extremely unsteady on his feet and Thomas was very clinging towards his foster carer. This was all last minute information that we ignored.

As soon as we got our children home, we were lucky enough to pick up a cancellation appointment with the local child development centre, courtesy of a prompt phone call from our new health visitor. We were shocked to realise that perhaps we had taken on significantly more than we realised. Both boys were terribly underweight: at the age of two-and-a-half they had the average weight of nine-month-old babies. They only had single word understanding (about the same as a one-year-old) and Thomas had very poor eye contact. They both seemed to have the attention span of a gnat and Christopher drove me insane with regular, incredibly shrill screaming; with excitement, with upset, you name it, he screamed about it.

It was confusing in those early weeks. On the one hand, Thomas and Christopher put on lots of weight as we stuffed them full of calorie-rich foods: extra butter, cream, cheese and sausages. We fried everything!

The dietician told us that extremely underweight children (which "drug children" often can be, especially if they have been premature) don't actually experience hunger.

And both boys made six months' developmental progress every three months for the first year. However, they also regressed behaviourally with regard to each other and were fiercely competitive for attention, mine in particular. They bit each other all the time. Their biting was so bad that while I was getting meals ready or hanging out the washing, I had to put them into "pens". I had three along the corridor, so that they weren't sharing a gate, otherwise their teeth would still have been sunk into each other when I turned around two minutes later. The lovely side-by-side double pushchair we had bought for them was a disaster in that respect.

I had worked really hard during introductions to ensure that Thomas, who was so terribly dependent on the foster mother, transferred his attachment to me. The downside of that was that Christopher, who everyone had been certain would make a good transition, bit me every single day for about six months as his morning greeting. They vied fiercely for my attention and it was utterly exhausting. Eventually, social services agreed to fund two afternoon sessions of two hours a week respite for me because, of course, they didn't sleep through the night either.

When we took them to nursery for the first time and put them alongside their peer group, it was utterly devastating.

These two endearing little sparrows whom we had

struggled with for the last three months – despite their remarkable progress which professionals had praised us for – stood out starkly, not only regarding their size but even more for their terrible developmental delay next to their great hulking peers with their advanced skills. At that point we knew we had brought home the consequences of drug abuse. Intellectually we knew the delay was also a result of prematurity and perhaps being in foster care too long, but we blamed the drugs. We wondered if they were ever going to go to normal school.

Around this time, we were asked if we would have a face-to-face meeting with the birth mum; she had previously declined to see us but had now changed her mind. Our twins' birth father had died of an accidental drug overdose when they were ten months old. We were very anxious but agreed and were glad that we had taken our social worker with us. Birth mum didn't look at all like a drug abuser. She was clean and not skinny and had clearly been well prepared to thank us for looking after her babies when she couldn't. Although she was turned out quite nicely and she was easy enough to talk to, her conversation was extremely repetitive and blaming of other people. However, we managed to get some key information about the boys' birth father and we felt we parted on good terms and that it was the right thing to have done. But we also came away wondering if she had cleaned up her act enough to have her children back and worried about this for a long time, as we continued to be given positive information about her during the following year. Our boys were still not legally adopted, so we felt quite vulnerable despite our social worker's reassurances.

After this meeting we had another real downer as we were asked to leave the local playgroup because I simply couldn't manage the twins' behaviour. They bit me, each other or somebody else. Or one would be having a tantrum on the floor so that I was unable to do anything with the other one. Seeing friends was difficult too, because my two were so overwhelming for the sweet little singletons. We were asked to leave ballet because one of my boys kept waving his willy around and the teacher was concerned about sexual abuse of the other children.

The weekends were too long so we went to church. Christopher managed to bite another child within two minutes and to my shame I blurted out, 'I'm so sorry, they're not mine, they're adopted!' One of the congregation stepped in and helped me and we discovered our first genuine source of support and kindness in the community. We went to church regularly for the next two years until the church moved. Through church we also found a wonderful music group.

Music was the key for our boys. The music leader thought that all parents of twins and multiples were terribly penalised, so only ever charged us for one child. They attended the music group right up until school.

That music group, called Skylarks, enabled me to see my children properly for the first time and to really recognise that despite the drug-abusing background and prematurity, there were two bright little boys in there just trying to find the right way out.

Christopher with his micro-attention span turned out

to be intrinsically musical. Music and rhythm harnessed his concentration. He is on the gifted and talented register for music. He started playing cornet at five and was playing in a band by six. He has perfect pitch and a beautiful treble voice. He also drives me insane as he is slapdash, and doesn't practise "properly". But actually he is happy doing what he does and I have to keep reminding myself that the first music class was the first time I really saw him for who he is.

Thomas discovered rhythm in that class. He sang like a foghorn but loved it. Now he sings boldly and strongly all the time. He also plays brass but hates to perform. Music has helped him gain a sense of time passing, and in the early days it helped him to wait for his turn.

School

Starting school was a challenge, partly because the boys were so delayed and partly because we had been parents for such a short time that we too felt catapulted into the system before we were ready. We chose a local school that had two reception classes. It was important to separate our twins to enable them to develop individual identities. They didn't really know their own names and were always answering to the wrong one. Right from the start it was clear that Christopher was okay and Thomas was miserable. Christopher loved his teacher and had a best friend very quickly. Thomas wasn't liked by his teacher and was seen as a disruptive and naughty child who wasn't learning what he was supposed to.

We started on a long process of battles with school. Extended family had noticed early on that Thomas had abnormal eye contact and autistic traits. This had also been noted by the child development centre and by us at home, but in the context of a relatively recent adoptive placement people were keen to let him settle first. The other question professionals had was whether Thomas was actually manifesting attachment disorder.

School persisted in telling us he was naughty. We eventually attended a parents' evening when the teacher said, 'Well, we know Thomas, don't we, by now? Basically the work is too difficult for him, but at least he doesn't upset the other children anymore.' We moved him to another school four weeks later and ten days after going to his new school, the staff requested a multi-professional meeting as they strongly suspected that Thomas was autistic. They were right, and he has made slow but steady and amazing progress with a Statement of Special Educational Needs and one-to-one support. He is on the gifted and talented register for art, and is clearly an intelligent little boy who has difficulty accessing the curriculum on his own.

Christopher is the one who has challenged us in his school with regard to his drug-misusing birth parents. All our children know about why they live with us. However, we kept that information completely confidential even from other adoptive families, as we had tuned into the concept from our adoption preparation groups that it was "the children's information". Different people had different reactions to us declining to discuss the children's background, and then we had to deal with different people and reactions depending on how the information came out. And it did come out.

In reception, Christopher excitedly put his hand up because he was able to give an example of words

SECTION II

beginning with "dr" – "drugs". He explained very clearly to his entire class that his daddy took drugs and was dead now and then suddenly, he became extremely upset.

The teacher, who did know about his history, failed to divert the tale in time. For a while there were some children who thought his adoptive father was a drug misuser, which was a bit awkward for a few school pickups. As we had carefully talked about how the information was their information and their story, and we hadn't told anyone except their teachers – not even our parents – we had to devise a rather quick damage limitation exercise. We encouraged our children to use their lifestory books to talk things through with family, but still struggled to explain adequately to them why we didn't think they should take them into school.

At 11 years old, our twins still completely lack any impulse control, so it was impossible to help them construct a sanitised version of their past for general discussions at school because neither of them could ever remember in time!

They went through a prolonged phase of about three years of being indiscriminately sociable with any passerby, informing them that they were adopted and that their parents took drugs. We seem to have survived and we still have local friends, but we do harbour the suspicion that half the town thinks that *we* are the drug misusers. This doesn't really seem to have harmed their class friendships or status with their peers at primary school.

Our twins start secondary school in September and we are again having discussions about some information being private, and that if the subject of adoption comes up, then it is sufficient for their peers to be told that their birth parents see them every year but are not able to look after them, and that they would rather not talk about it in detail. New school, new area. We shall see.

Whenever the subject of drugs comes up we return to the lifestory books that we prepared for them (social services failed to manage that and it was left to us). The books talk about their birth parents loving them but being on drugs, which made them confused about how to look after them and forgetful about visiting. They were three when we made their lifestory books and we haven't yet updated them. When we have conversations about what taking drugs means these days, we talk about drugs being medicines that people don't need but buy anyway although it is against the law. Because they don't need the medicines, these drugs make them confused and then they get used to them and can't stop taking them. We talk about their birth parents making a wrong choice when they were younger, and finding it impossible to fix the wrong choice after all this time. The boys are consistent in wanting to bring their birth mother to live with us to help her learn how to make good choices. For now, we have opted to tell them that the courts would not permit that, as they need to keep their adoptive parents and home for themselves.

We had a birth child, William, 18 months after adopting the twins, and 18 months after that their birth mother also had another baby who joined us when he was 12 months old. We went from nought to four children in four years. We probably wouldn't recommend it!

Richard was tiny, even smaller than his twin brothers had been. However, he was born only six weeks early. His mother had an emergency caesarean because she went into heart failure as a consequence of her drug use. Her survival during the pregnancy and immediately afterwards was in question. Because the twins had been so much older coming to us, they had already been tested for HIV and hepatitis B and C and we knew that they were negative. It was a whole different scenario with Richard.

We found out that the boys' birth mother was pregnant from their paternal grandfather, with whom we had regular contact as he was local to us and we got on well. She had moved from the area, so we contacted the original social worker to remind her that we had always said we would be open to any further siblings that came along. We did a lot of soul searching about how we felt about HIV and hepatitis. We knew that mum had hepatitis C but her HIV status was unknown as she had consistently refused to be tested. We knew that her first husband had died of AIDS.

We contacted our local HIV and liver specialists and had very helpful discussions with them.

We learned that the vast majority of children who get HIV from their pregnant mother stay healthy throughout childhood and certainly seem to be living healthily into at least their 20s and longer these days. We were completely reassured that normal family life would not pose any risk to the other children or ourselves from an infection point of view.

We were also informed that we could be reasonably optimistic that if the first two antibody tests were negative, it was extremely unlikely that the baby would be affected, though there are a few very rare cases which are identified at the third test following two negative ones. With regard to hepatitis C, we again found that there was a negligible risk to the other children and ourselves if we adhered to routine hygiene care and covered open wounds. It also seems to be an area in which there is ongoing progress and research, and even if he were to test positive, there would be the real possibility of eradication treatment in adulthood.

We realised that we had completely changed our position: we now had an autistic child, and were prepared to take on a child with a potentially life-limiting condition, which was most likely to have consequences for him in young adulthood rather than childhood.

Fortunately, Richard was given the "all clear" for both conditions six months after being placed with us.

We had thought that Richard might be more affected by the drug use as he had been exposed for longer. Also, his mother's health was extremely poor and his growth in the uterus had been restricted because of this. In fact, he is so tiny that he met the criteria to be given growth hormone injections. Children who are growth retarded as a result of placenta problems can be given growth hormone injections, but they have to be started before school age and they have a better outcome if started very young. We decided that Richard had a big enough personality to cope with being a small boy and a small adult, and he had enough on his plate without adding weekly, or it might have been monthly, injections. He has managed to creep up from the bottom of the growth chart over the last six years.

It seems that the benefits of growing inside the pregnant mother far outweigh the risks of the drugs: babies do better the longer they are inside despite maternal drug misuse. Certainly this is true for our son as he is clearly a bright and able child. We always save him until last on parents' evening at school because it is so nice to have one child that the teacher basically says "great" about – and that includes behaviour!

One thing that was difficult for Richard was coping in the reception class. He never managed a full day. We tried really hard in the summer term, but his behaviour and learning deteriorated to the point that he was excluded for hitting and biting. His teacher and the headmaster were really shocked. They agreed for him to return to half days and the problems miraculously evaporated over three days. This was with him getting up at 7am and being in bed and asleep usually by 6.30pm. By the end of the first term in year one, he was managing full days and his behaviour was mostly okay. He then had sudden catch-up and by the summer term was managing gymnastics, beavers and tenor horn music lessons. We hadn't planned so many after-school activities, but Richard was always getting his brothers' instruments out to play, and in the end we took him to the music teacher, really expecting him to say he was too small. Instead, after 20 minutes of trying every brass instrument in the room, we were lumbered with, 'Gosh, this one's got real aptitude! Would he like to borrow an instrument for a while to see how he gets on?' After six weeks, it was

SECTION II

87

clear that there was going to be no holding him back. It makes for an endearing appearance though, as he is so very tiny and a tenor horn is pretty much as big as he is. After a term, he is playing in the local training band. Yes, he definitely can manage without that growth hormone.

It is fascinating having Richard after the twins and also knowing their older brother and maternal grandparents, aunt and uncle. They all have similar mannerisms. Christopher walks just like his grandfather and looks just like his great aunt. Apparently he talks just as much as his mother did as a child. Actually, the whole family talks a lot! And they are all rather bird-like in build.

Thomas and Christopher clearly have additional needs. Christopher has recently spent several weeks with both legs in plaster and now wears splints on his feet and legs to help with his walking. He wears glasses and has braces and he dribbles if he is concentrating on something and has forgotten to close his mouth. He has had extra help for English. He has to sit alone at a desk in class, otherwise he simply cannot get on with his work. But he maintains a good solid average across the board despite his general slapdash attitude, and is a wonderful cornet player; at the age of three we believed he would be in a special school.

Thomas is a happy child who can read and write. Yes, he is 11 and functions at the academic level of a seven or eight-year-old, but he is otherwise intelligent and gifted at art. (Remember, that in 2010, ten per cent of boys leaving primary school in England and Wales had a reading age of between seven and eight years, so he is only in the bottom ten per cent, not on his own.) We believe a lot of the twins' difficulties can be attributed to parental drug misuse, but there is little about them that isn't seen in other premature children. Richard was six weeks early but at the age of six is performing at the top end of his class in English and maths, and he has been able to do a somersault in the air from standing since he was three, so there is nothing wrong with his co-ordination.

Something all the boys have in common is wanting to help their birth mother stop taking drugs. Only Richard's birth father is still alive. We have set up and had successful face-to-face contact three times in the last four years with birth mum and Richard's birth father. All the meetings, despite the associated stresses, have absolutely been the right thing for us as a family.

At the first meeting, our autistic son, Thomas, who really doesn't like physical contact, was ensconced on his birth mum's lap within two minutes of getting into the room. It was extraordinary. It was as though he had just come home and they had never been apart. Anyone could see the instant bond. It was pretty much the same on the later visits, though he's too big for her lap now. I was very shocked at the time and think that if we had had that contact earlier in our time together as a family, I would have found it quite threatening. These days I recognise the strength of our parent–child relationship, and am able to be grateful that my children have had this opportunity to remain connected to their roots.

Christopher, normally so socially confident and "in your face", had a major case of shyness during that first meeting that was most unexpected. On subsequent visits, he started to realise what his birth mum's problems mean in terms of her ability to look after them. She tells a different version of how his father died (for instance, not from a drug overdose) each time we meet up and gets confused about the previous meetings we have had. It is heartrending to see Christopher acquire this insight and there is usually some behavioural fall-out for a week or two after, but so far, not of an order that would prevent us having the meetings.

At our last contact, it was clear birth mum was unwell. She was breathless, unkempt and not frightfully sweet smelling; it reinforced our gratitude that she has felt able to make these meetings. We are aware from the social worker that she sees the direct contact as something to boast about to her friends: although her children have been taken away and adopted, she still sees them. Unfortunately, whenever she has a meeting with us, she fails to bother to see her oldest son for his contact afterwards.

Living with a disability

It may seem slightly odd, but to the outsider, three of our five children have disabilities. Christopher, we suppose, has a mild cerebral palsy. Thomas is autistic and still wets his pants during the day. Our second birth child has a swallowing problem and is tube fed. This was a real blow after a difficult surprise pregnancy. Fortunately, he is making better progress than professionals expected, and he is just starting to manage pureed baby foods, though he still needs the tube for fluids.

Over tea just yesterday, our middle child, William, called Christopher a "spaz". Outraged, Christopher came stomping into the kitchen, complaining that his brother said he was disabled. 'I'm not disabled, am I? Just because I wear splints and dribble!'

Thomas got involved. 'No! That's not disabled. You are disabled, William, not Christopher. You don't even know what you are talking about!'

They eventually remembered that it's not meant to matter if you are disabled or not because everyone has something they are good at and everyone is special. The name- calling brother ended up not being deemed as special as the twins, because he was 'just a surprise' whereas they were 'specially chosen'. They managed to come up with Christopher being good at music, Thomas being good at art and William being good at maths. Needless to say, the saga continues. I think it illustrates though, that just like in every other family, there is name-calling and side-taking, and it takes a while to sort through.

Thomas has a number of worries that have changed over time. He used to ask what job he could do as a grown up for which he would not have to be able to read. It is wonderful that he can now read, as we can reassure him that with time and practice he will master other things he finds difficult. He is very clear though, that he does not want to get married or have his own children, as that would be too tricky for him.

I think that our genuinely challenged children mostly do not see themselves as having either special needs or being disabled, which we are pleased about. We hope they hang on to this self-belief through secondary school. It also seems that no matter how annoying and exhausting they are at times, other people mostly seem to be charmed by them and their positive personalities shine through.

We are very grateful to our local carers' resource

office, which sent round a volunteer at the request of
our health visitor when we first had the boys. They
explained about DLA (Disability Living Allowance)
and helped us fill in the forms (a marathon). It's quite
depressing dealing with forms like that as it emphasises
all the negative things about your child. It can make you
feel really guilty, listing all sorts of things that your child
cannot do that others of the same age manage just fine.

We have used our DLA for buying a new large-tub,
extra-fast spin washing machine, for music and ballet
lessons, and we use it now mainly for extra child
care. I finally acknowledged that I was going to cause
permanent damage if I tried to do educational things
with my autistic son, as it simply precipitated a flare-up
of some kind. We have paid for someone to come in
after school to do daily reading and homework with
him. The money helps to make sure that each of the
boys gets some individual adult attention most days. We
also use it for story tapes. When you have an intelligent
child who can't read but wants to be read to, they are a
complete lifesaver.

Promoting resilience and independence
This is hard. Really, we think our boys are very
vulnerable and Christopher in particular, is very easily
led. We've ended up moving to a smaller town to a place
just five minutes from the town centre. In this new, safer
and smaller environment, our twins have suddenly gained
more independence. They can go to the local library on
their own. They are allowed 30 minutes free computer
time per day and the librarian is happy to be telephoned
to check they are where I think they are. There is a
single road to cross with a pedestrian crossing so that
they can go to the local shop. In September, they will

walk to school, eventually on their own. As there is only one secondary school in town, everyone they will know of school age is likely to go there. Currently, they are feeling very grown up!

What and who have helped and what has not

It has helped having as much information as possible about parental drug abuse, HIV and hepatitis. It has helped to talk to, and be reassured by, the doctor running the development clinic for children of drug-misusing mothers.

Really, once the issue of life-limiting illness and infection risks had been addressed, the specific issue of parenting children born to a drug-addicted mother faded completely into the background. We feel that we have been lucky to have an old-fashioned holistic health visitor who has looked after us all, who has been in the area for ever, and who always knew where to get help.

Our own social worker is also exceptional. Being referred to the local child development centre within the first month, and referred a couple of years later to a psychologist who was experienced in adoption and attachment as well as autistic spectrum disorders, has been key for us as a family.

My husband and I have changed roles in that I work full time and he works part time. Although this wasn't the plan, losing his job six months after we got the twins meant he was at home and I went screaming back to work. It turns out he is better at the after-school stuff and organising children than I am, but hey, I'm still better at organising what we are going to eat and when. My husband's current work place has been amazingly kind and supportive and has enabled him to take time off when necessary.

- Talk to as many parents of adopted children as you can.

- Recognise that a huge amount really is the luck of the draw: two children with virtually identical paper descriptions going forward for adoption can have very different outcomes.

- Make an appointment to see the local paediatrician who does the follow-up clinic for the local children of drug-misusing parents. There will be one. You may need to use your health visitor or your GP to get you in the door. See them before you are committed.

- Immediately your child arrives, ask your GP to refer you to the child development centre for monitoring their progress.

- See your local HIV and hepatitis specialists. You will need to go to teaching hospitals for this usually as they will have the up-to-date information about life expectancy and treatments.

- Wait for an older child if you are very worried about the impact of drugs, so that you can see whether and how they have been affected.

- Close your eyes and jump and take that very young baby even if their mother did take unknown drug cocktails,

- Take the opportunity to meet birth parents and have your picture taken with them. Get the meeting videoed if possible; edit out the bad bits so you can at least show your children that you were all nice to each other if they never have the opportunity for contact.

- Push social services to arrange direct contact for your children at the right time for them, even if no contact at all was recommended at placement.

- Try to find another adoptive family whom you get on with and can bounce your worries off – though it turns out we all worry about different things.

- Try to remember that although nurture can outweigh nature, both will come through, and nobody has a perfect child–parent relationship all the time.

- Develop a thick skin for when the entire town has been informed that you are a drug abuser, and acquire a ready response to deal with subsequent questions!

SECTION II

References

BAAF (2007) *Reducing the Risks of Environmental Tobacco Smoke for Looked After Children and their Carers*, Practice Note 51, London: BAAF

BAAF (2008) *Guidelines for the Testing of Looked After Children who are at Risk of a Blood-borne Infection*, Practice Note 53, London: BAAF

Brocklesby E, Vaillant JL, McCormick A, Mandelli D and Mather M (2009) 'Substance misuse in pregnancy: an unrecognised and misdiagnosed problem for a child', *Seen and Heard*, 19:1, March 2009, pp 22-32

FAS Aware (2011) *Parenting Children Affected by Fetal Alcohol Syndrome: A guide for daily living*, Ministry for Children and Families Edition, British Columbia, Canada; available at www.fasaware.co.uk/education_docs/daily_guide_for_living.pdf

Forrester D and Harwin J (2011) *Parents who Misuse Drugs and Alcohol: Effective interventions in social work and child protection*, Chichester: Wiley-Blackwell

Phillips R (ed) (2004) *Children Exposed to Substance Misuse: Implications for family placement*, London: BAAF

Useful organisations

Alcohol Concern

A main source of reliable information and support on all aspects of alcohol misuse and its effects.

27 Swinton Street
London
WC1X 9NW
Tel: 020 3907 8480
www.alcoholconcern.org.uk

Contact a Family

Excellent national charity that provides information and other support for the families of disabled children, whatever their condition or disability.

209–211 City Road
London
EC1V 1JN
Tel: 020 7608 8700

Freephone helpline: 0808 808 3555

www.cafamily.org.uk

DrugWise

Probably the best organisation for overall information on drug use and its impacts.

www.drugwise.org.uk

The Lulluby Trust

Provides information and support aimed at preventing unexpected deaths in infancy and promoting infant health.

11 Belgrave Road

London

SW1V 1RB

Tel (general enquiries): 020 7802 3200

Freephone helpline: 080 8802 6868

www.fsid.org.uk

National Organisation on Fetal Alcohol Syndrome (NOFAS) – UK

Dedicated to eliminating birth defects caused by alcohol consumption during pregnancy and to improving the quality of life for all those affected – children, adults, families and carers. NOFAS runs a helpline for all those concerned as well as family support groups, playgroups for children and a regular newsletter.

022 Southbank House

Black Prince Road

Lambeth

London

SE1 7SJ

Helpline: 020 8458 5951

www.nofas-uk.org

Patient.co.uk

A good source of evidence-based articles and information covering a wide variety of health issues, including premature babies and their problems, with further links to specific influential factors such substance misuse.

www.patient.co.uk/doctor/Premature-Babies-and-their-Problems.htm

The Tilda Goldberg Centre

Lists further academic research reviews of evidence related to drug and alcohol misuse in pregnancy specifically aimed at foster carers and adopters.

www.beds.ac.uk/goldbergcentre